WACKY MAD LIBS III

How To Play Mad Libs:

In this pad you'll find different kinds of stories with some words left out. One person picks out a story. This person is the only one who knows the story before it's finished. Without telling the story, he/she asks the other players for words to fill up the blank spaces in the stories, then he/she writes them in the blanks. When the story is complete, he/she reads it aloud. After everyone stops laughing — someone *else* gets to pick a story and ask for words.

To fill in the blanks in each of the stories, you'll need to know the following parts of speech: NOUN; ADJECTIVE; VERB; ADVERB.

This edition of MAD LIBS is a selection taken from twelve full-length editions of MAD LIBS published by Price/Stern/Sloan Publishers, Inc., 410 North La Cienega Blvd., Los Angeles, Calif. 90048. They are available at book, gift, and stationery stores or directly from Price/Stern/Sloan Publishers, Inc.

ISBN 0-590-33184-1

Copyright © 1958, 1959, 1962, 1965, 1968, 1970, 1974, 1976, 1977, 1978, 1986 by Price/Stern/Sloan Publishers, Inc., Los Angeles.

60 59 58 57 56 55 54 53 52 51   3/0

Printed in the U.S.A.   40

SCHOLASTIC INC
New York Toronto London Au

W9-AUF-396

A NOUN, as you know, is the name of a person, place, or thing, such as <u>friend</u>, <u>school</u>, or <u>book</u>. Plural means more than one.

An ADJECTIVE is a word that describes a noun, such as <u>sticky</u>, <u>quiet</u>, or <u>jumpy</u>.

A VERB is an action word. It tells what a noun does, such as <u>run</u>, <u>read</u>, or <u>scream</u>.

An ADVERB tells how something is done. It describes a verb and often ends in "ly." <u>Easily</u>, <u>bravely</u>, and <u>truthfully</u> are adverbs.

Here's a short example to get you going:

The best thing you can do for a cold is to stay in your

_____roller coaster_____, get plenty of rest, and drink lots of
           NOUN

__maple syrup__. For those aches and __umbrellas__,
   A LIQUID   PLURAL NOUN

take aspirin every _____642_____ hours, and be sure to call
                  A NUMBER

your ____alarm clock____ if your temperature goes up. Some
           NOUN

_____purple_____ tea or _____elephant_____ soup can
  ADJECTIVE   AN ANIMAL

also help a nasty cold. And don't forget to _____attack_____
                                  VERB (PRESENT TENSE)

your runny nose with soft tissues. Otherwise, you could end up

looking like Rudolph, the red-nosed _____orangutan_____.
                                       AN ANIMAL

MOVIE STUDIO TOUR

Good afternoon ladies and gentlemen, I am your guide for the famous Universal Studio Tour, one of California's

_____ attractions. First, on the right, you
ADJECTIVE ENDING IN "EST"

will see a huge fin which belongs to the terrifying

_____ used in the movie, "Jaws." Next, you will
A FISH

meet the Bionic _____ and see how it performs
NOUN

_____ feats of strength. Then you will see the
ADJECTIVE

famous star, _____, in a scene from the movie,
NAME OF PERSON IN ROOM

_____. Then you will see Universal's daredevil
TITLE OF A MOVIE

stunt _____ who can fall from the unbelievable
PLURAL NOUN

height of _____ feet and land safely on their
A NUMBER

_____. Following that, a flash flood will engulf
PLURAL NOUN

our _____ bus, and finally you will meet Frank-
ADJECTIVE

enstein, the famous _____. Please remain in your
AN OCCUPATION OR JOB

_____ at all times.
PLURAL NOUN

AD FOR A NEW STEREO

Hey, all you music lovers, here is a chance to get a

_____ new _____ stereo.
　　　ADJECTIVE　　　　　　　　LAST NAME OF PERSON IN ROOM

This set will play _____ records and
　　　　　　　　　　　　　　　ADJECTIVE

_____ cassettes. It comes with _____
　　　ADJECTIVE　　　　　　　　　　　　　　　　　　A NUMBER

cassettes and five _____. It has _____
　　　　　　　　　　　PLURAL NOUN　　　　　　　　　　A NUMBER

dynamic speakers. Each speaker is covered with imitation

_____ guaranteed not to fade or
　　　A KIND OF MATERIAL

_____. This stereo is _____ and
VERB (PRESENT TENSE)　　　　　　　　　　TWO LETTERS

_____; maybe even _____.
TWO MORE LETTERS　　　　　　　　　　THREE LETTERS

Listen to your favorite _____ on this stereo with its
　　　　　　　　　　　　　PLURAL NOUN

fantastic, _____ sound. And best news of all, it
　　　　　　　ADJECTIVE

will only cost you _____ dollars.
　　　　　　　　　　A NUMBER

THE SPACE SHUTTLE

In 1981, the U.S. launched the first real Space

_____. It was called a _____ Shuttle
   NOUN   NOUN

because it not only went up into _____ space,
                               ADJECTIVE

it also came back. It was named the "Columbia" and was piloted

by two brave _____. They had practiced
                   PLURAL NOUN

_____ for two years and were expert
  VERB ENDING IN "ING"

_____. The Columbia took off from
     PLURAL NOUN

_____ using its powerful first stage
       A CITY

_____. At an altitude of _____
   PLURAL NOUN   A NUMBER

feet, it went into orbit around the _____. After
                           SOMETHING ROUND

_____ orbits, the Shuttle landed _____
    A NUMBER   ADVERB

at _____. It was a _____ day for
     A PLACE   ADJECTIVE

the U.S. Space Program.

AN EXCUSE LETTER

Dear Mr. _____,
         LAST NAME OF BOY IN ROOM

I hope you will excuse _____ for being
                        NAME OF GIRL IN ROOM

absent from your _____ _____ class.
                    ADJECTIVE   **A SCHOOL SUBJECT**

I know she has been absent _____ times,
                              A NUMBER

but she had to stay home to help her father build a

_____. She also had a dreadful cold in her
        NOUN

_____, and her nose was _____.
        NOUN   **VERB ENDING IN "ING"**

She still would have made it, but then her alarm clock broke

and wouldn't _____. You are her most
              VERB (PRESENT TENSE)

_____ teacher, and I hope you will not
        ADJECTIVE

_____ her or give her a
              VERB (PRESENT TENSE)

failing _____.
            NOUN

Signed,

Her Mother

TRACK MEETS

For years, everyone thought that the four-minute mile was a

_____ dream. Now every Tom, Dick and
      ADJECTIVE

_____ can run the mile in four minutes due
   A SILLY FIRST NAME

to new training methods. Distance runners have to give up

_____ and _____. They have to
VERB ENDING IN "ING"   VERB ENDING IN "ING"

eat plenty of _____ and lots of fresh
               A FOOD

_____ vegetables. Then they must practice. Every
   A COLOR

morning they _____ until they're exhausted.
       VERB (PRESENT TENSE)

Then they take a _____ shower and do two hours
         ADJECTIVE

of _____-ups. This strengthens their
   VERB (PRESENT TENSE)

_____. _____ has run the
PLURAL NOUN   NAME OF PERSON IN ROOM

mile in less than five minutes, but of course he (she) was riding

on a _____.
   A VEHICLE

EASTER VACATION

Easter vacations usually fall around Easter time. The schools

are closed and all the _____ get
                            PLURAL NOUN

_____ weeks off. There are a lot of things to
       A NUMBER

do on Easter vacation. Some kids loaf around and watch the

_____. Others go outside and play _____,
    NOUN   **A GAME**

while more ambitious students spend their time studying their

_____ books so they will grow up to become
      ADJECTIVE

_____. Kids also color _____ eggs.
 AN OCCUPATION OR JOB   **ADJECTIVE**

Here's how you color an egg: First mix a package of

_____ dye in a bowl full of _____.
      ADJECTIVE   **A LIQUID**

Then dip the _____ in the bowl and rinse it off with
                  NOUN

_____. Then after it dries, you can paint on it with
   A LIQUID

a brush. Then you show it to your friends who will say, "Boy, what

a _____ egg!"
       ADJECTIVE

CALIFORNIA

California is the _____ state in the
ADJECTIVE ENDING IN "EST"

Union. It was admitted in 1850 and since then, the number of

_____ who _____ here has
PLURAL NOUN   VERB (PRESENT TENSE)

increased every year. It is noted for its _____
ADJECTIVE

climate, its _____ air, and its _____
ADJECTIVE   ADJECTIVE

beaches and palm trees. Grapes, which are used to make fine

_____, grow in Northern California. There are
A LIQUID

many _____ movie and television studios in
ADJECTIVE

Los Angeles, which is the home of famous stars such as

_____ and _____. The
NAME OF BOY IN ROOM   NAME OF GIRL IN ROOM

California State Flower is the _____ and the
A FLOWER

Capital is Sacramento where Governor _____
A MOVIE STAR

lives. If you are looking for a _____ place to
ADJECTIVE

retire and spend the rest of your life _____,
VERB ENDING IN "ING"

California is the perfect _____.
NOUN

A FAN LETTER

Dear _____,
NAME OF A SINGER

I think your group, the _____ _____ is
VERB ENDING IN "ING" PLURAL NOUN

the greatest! My most favorite songs are "I'd _____
VERB (PRESENT TENSE)

For You" and "I'm Cryin' My _____ Out Over
PLURAL NOUN

You." I think you are a better singer than Michael Jackson or even

_____. I love it when you come on stage dressed
A FAMOUS PERSON

up like a _____ _____. And when
ADJECTIVE NOUN

you play the electric _____, I can't help scream-
NOUN

ing and squealing, and _____. Please send
VERB ENDING IN "ING"

me an autographed _____. Every night I will
NOUN

sleep with it under my _____. Signed, your
NOUN

devoted _____.
NOUN

ANIMAL QUESTIONS AND ANSWERS

QUESTION: Why do camels have _____?

PLURAL NOUN

ANSWER: Camels have to go for days without food or

_____. Their humps are made of

A LIQUID

_____, on which they live.

A SUBSTANCE

QUESTION: Can dogs talk?

ANSWER: A dog is talking when he wags his _____,

NOUN

or when he barks. If a dog wags his tail, it can

mean _____ or _____!

A GREETING _AN EXCLAMATION_

QUESTION: When frightened, does an ostrich stick its

_____ in the sand?

NOUN

ANSWER: No, it can run away very fast because it has such

long _____.

PLURAL NOUN

QUESTION: What is the biggest land animal alive today?

ANSWER: The elephant. It weighs _____ tons.

A NUMBER

It has a _____ trunk which it uses to

ADJECTIVE

squirt _____ on its back when it is hot.

A LIQUID

SLEEPING BEAUTY

Once, a king and queen had a _____ daughter
                                    ADJECTIVE

and invited seven _____ fairies to be the child's
                        ADJECTIVE

godmothers. But a wicked _____ cast a spell on
                                NOUN

the little girl. On the morning of her fifteenth birthday, the

princess _____ and fell into a _____
            VERB (PAST TENSE)   ADJECTIVE

sleep. She slept _____ for one hundred years.
                        ADVERB

Then a handsome young _____ came riding up
                                NOUN

to the castle. He dismounted, went inside, and found that

all the _____ were asleep. He searched every
            PLURAL NOUN

_____ and finally he _____
        NOUN   VERB (PAST TENSE)

the princess. She was so _____ that he could not
                                ADJECTIVE

help himself. He kissed her, and she woke up at once. He married

her, and they lived _____ ever after.
                            ADVERB

INVITATION TO A DANCE

As a member of the _____ class of
                    ADJECTIVE

_____, you are invited to the annual Spring Dance.
NAME OF A SCHOOL

Dress is _____. But we hope you will not wear
          ADJECTIVE

_____ or dirty _____. Music
PLURAL NOUN   PLURAL NOUN

will be provided by the "Rolling _____" fea-
                                  PLURAL NOUN

turing Bruce Springsteen and _____. The
                              NAME OF PERSON IN ROOM

dance will be held as usual in _____ which
                                A PLACE

will be specially decorated with red, white, and blue

_____, and many colored _____. The price
PLURAL NOUN   PLURAL NOUN

of admission is _____ dollars and this includes one
                A NUMBER

free glass of _____. Boys will be expected to buy
              A LIQUID

a corsage of _____ for their dates.
             PLURAL NOUN

CAR RACING

Parnelli Jones and _____ finished in that
　　　　　　　　　　　NAME OF PERSON IN ROOM

order in the famous _____ Speedway 500 Auto
　　　　　　　　　　　　　A CITY

Race. Jones was last year's International_____
　　　　　　　　　　　　　　　　　　　　　　ADJECTIVE

Champion. He drove a modified _____ with dual
　　　　　　　　　　　　　　　　　NOUN

_____ and a _____ suspension.
PLURAL NOUN　　　　　　　ADJECTIVE

Racing against Jones were a custom-made _____ cylinder
　　　　　　　　　　　　　　　　　　　　A NUMBER

_____, and a four-wheel-drive _____.
AN ITALIAN WORD　　　　　　　　　　　　　A GERMAN WORD

_____, who drove a _____,
A MOVIE STAR　　　　　　　　　　　　A FRENCH WORD

was leading in the 40th lap, but went into a skid on the

_____ turn and had a flat_____. Then
ADJECTIVE　　　　　　　　　　　　　　　NOUN

Jones _____ to the front and won easily by eight
　　　　VERB (PAST TENSE)

_____. Afterwards Jones said, "It was a
PLURAL NOUN

_____ race. The other drivers are all
　　ADJECTIVE

_____ sports, and I would like to
　　ADJECTIVE

_____ them all."
VERB

SILLY SUPERSTITIONS

Although we believe ourselves to be _____
                                        ADVERB

civilized, most of us are really _____ at heart
                                   PLURAL NOUN

because we still believe in _____ superstitions
                              ADJECTIVE

that began while man still lived in _____.
                                      PLURAL NOUN

Some of these superstitions are:

1. If you spill salt, throw some over your left _____.
                                                   NOUN

2. If a black _____ runs in front of you, you are
                AN ANIMAL

   in trouble.

3. If you break a _____, you will have
                     NOUN

   _____ years of _____ luck.
      A NUMBER   ADJECTIVE

4. Never _____ under a ladder.
           VERB (PRESENT TENSE)

5. If your _____ itches, it means you will have
              NOUN

   a visitor.

6. If you want to keep vampires away, always wear a

   _____ on a string around your _____.
      A FOOD   NOUN

THE NEW TEACHER

"Good morning, students. I am your new teacher,

_____. I am going to teach you _____.
NAME OF PERSON IN ROOM   VERB ENDING IN "ING"

We will start off with a _____ test. First, I want
ADJECTIVE

you all to make sure your _____ are sharpened
PLURAL NOUN

and that you have plenty of _____ paper. During
ADJECTIVE

this test I will not allow any _____. If you want
VERB ENDING IN "ING"

to _____, raise your _____ and say,
VERB (PRESENT TENSE)   NOUN

'_____!' Here is the first question: Name
AN EXCLAMATION

ten _____ that live in the _____
PLURAL NOUN   ADJECTIVE

mountains of _____. You have only five minutes
A COUNTRY

so you will have to write _____."
ADVERB

BOWLING

Bowling was invented in ancient times by the _____
ADJECTIVE

Russian Czar, _____, who was also known as
NAME OF BOY IN ROOM

Ivan the _____. The Czar would line up a bunch
ADJECTIVE

of his favorite _____ and then roll a giant
PLURAL NOUN

cannon ball at them. When he knocked them all down, he

would wave a _____ _____ and
NOUN ADVERB

yell, "_____!" And this is where we, today, get
AN EXCLAMATION

the expression "_____." Today, bowling is
A NONSENSE WORD

a _____ business. People roll balls made of
ADJECTIVE

_____ down smooth wooden alleys to knock
A KIND OF MATERIAL

over ten _____. Most bowlers belong to leagues.
PLURAL NOUN

This means the bowling team has a sponsor who gets to put his

_____ on each of their _____.
NOUN PLURAL NOUN

Bowling is fun and good exercise for developing your

_____.
PLURAL NOUN

AN ADVERTISEMENT

Men! Is your hair turning _____? Is it getting a little
                             A COLOR

_____ on top? If that's the case, then let our famous
ADJECTIVE

plastic _____ use the latest techniques
        AN OCCUPATION OR JOB (PLURAL)

to graft tiny follicles of _____ to your scalp. No
                            PLURAL NOUN

one can tell if your hair is _____ or not. And you will
                              ADJECTIVE

be very delighted to discover that you look _____ years
                                              A NUMBER

younger and women will say, "_____!"
                              AN EXCLAMATION

LETTER OF COMPLAINT

Dear Marvo Hair Co.,

I paid you _____ dollars for a _____ trans-
           A NUMBER   **NOUN**

plant. I did everything you told me. I started by soaking my head

every day in _____ and washed my hair with
             A LIQUID

_____. But now my _____ smells
ANOTHER LIQUID   **NOUN**

like rotten _____. I am suing because I am as bald
            A FOOD

as a _____.
     NOUN

CUSTER'S LAST WHATCHAMACALLIT

This is the story of Custer's last _____. General

NOUN

Custer was a _____ in the Civil War, sometimes

NOUN

called the War Between the _____. He was

PLURAL NOUN

a vain man with long, yellow _____ and a

PLURAL NOUN

_____ disposition.

ADJECTIVE

In 1876, settlers were _____ into the West.

VERB ENDING IN "ING"

This made the Indians _____ and they started

ADJECTIVE

_____.

VERB ENDING IN "ING"

In 1876, President Grant sent Custer with a troop of United States

_____ into the West to protect American

PLURAL NOUN

_____. Custer followed the Indian force

PLURAL NOUN

and set up camp at the little _____ Horn. The

ADJECTIVE

next morning, over _____ Indians attacked and that

A NUMBER

was that. Custer's last words were, "_____

AN EXCLAMATION

_____!"

VISIT TO A MUSEUM

Last week, all of the _____ in our class at
PLURAL NOUN

_____ School got into a _____ and
NAME OF A SCHOOL   A VEHICLE

went to the County Museum of _____ History.
ADJECTIVE

First, we saw a model of a cave _____ sitting by a
NOUN

fire, roasting a _____ on a stick. Then, we saw all
NOUN

kinds of stuffed _____ which looked as if they were
PLURAL NOUN

really _____. There were suits of armor that were
ADJECTIVE

worn by the ancient _____. And we saw some
PLURAL NOUN

old _____ jewelry that had been worn by
ADJECTIVE

_____ who was Queen of _____.
NAME OF GIRL IN ROOM   A PLACE

All in all, it was a _____ trip.
ADJECTIVE

SALE OF THE CENTURY

_____ has announced that his _____
A TV ACTOR   ADJECTIVE

clothing store in the heart of downtown _____ is
                                          A CITY

having a _____ sale of all merchandise, including
          ADJECTIVE

_____ suits and slightly irregular _____.
ADJECTIVE   PLURAL NOUN

Men's cable-knit _____, only $10.98. Handwoven
                  PLURAL NOUN

Italian _____, half price. Beautiful cashmere
         PLURAL NOUN

_____, $35.00. Genuine imported _____
PLURAL NOUN   A COLOR

_____ shoes, silk _____, and
ADJECTIVE   PLURAL NOUN

women's wool _____, all at rock-bottom prices.
              PLURAL NOUN

This is a chance to get some really _____
                                     ADJECTIVE

bargains.

THE PHOTO SESSION

GIRL: I would like to have a color photograph taken. Is this the

_____ place?
ADJECTIVE

BOY: Yes. I take photographs of _____,
A GATHERING OF PEOPLE

weddings, and sometimes even _____.
PLURAL NOUN

GIRL: I want a picture for my school _____ book.
NOUN

BOY: All right. Please sit on this stool while I put some film in

my _____.
NOUN

GIRL: I'll sit this way so you can get my _____ side.
ADJECTIVE

BOY: All right. I think I'll use this 500-watt

_____ to light your hair. Now just hold still.
NOUN

Good! You look like _____.
A MOVIE STAR

GIRL: Everyone says that. Do you think I need makeup on my

_____?
A PART OF THE FACE

BOY: No, I'm all set. Now say, "_____." There!
A FOOD

You can have the _____ Monday.
PLURAL NOUN

ABE LINCOLN

Abraham Lincoln was the 16th American to be elected President of the United _____. Lincoln is famous
PLURAL NOUN

for his _____ Proclamation. He also kept the
ADJECTIVE

South from seceding from the _____. Lincoln is
A DIRECTION

noted for his wise sayings. He said, "A _____ divided
NOUN

against itself cannot _____," and "The Lord
VERB (PRESENT TENSE)

prefers _____-looking men. That is why he made
ADJECTIVE

so many of them." Lincoln had a _____ beard
ADJECTIVE

and usually wore a tall _____ hat. There is
ADJECTIVE

a beautiful monument to Lincoln in Washington D.C. that is

visited every year by thousands of _____. It is
PLURAL NOUN

called the _____ Memorial.
LAST NAME OF BOY IN ROOM

THE PRIZE FIGHT

Good evening, sports _____. I'm speaking to
                        PLURAL NOUN

you from ringside at the famous _____ and bring-
                                A FAMOUS BUILDING

ing you a blow-by-blow description of the _____
                                          ADJECTIVE

fight between Rocky _____ and the
                    LAST NAME OF PERSON IN ROOM

_____ champion, Slugger _____.
ADJECTIVE   LAST NAME OF ANOTHER PERSON IN ROOM

As the bell rings for round _____, Rocky moves
                            A NUMBER

_____ to the center of the ring and throws a
ADVERB

_____ right to Slugger's _____. But
ADJECTIVE   NOUN

Slugger blocks the punch with his _____ and hits
                                  NOUN

Rocky right on the _____ with a tremendous
                   NOUN

uppercut that knocks him _____ on
                         ADJECTIVE

his back. The referee is counting and the fans are cheering

_____. _____! What a
ADVERB   AN EXCLAMATION

_____ fight this has been!
ADJECTIVE

PUBLIC SERVICE COMMERCIALS

Are you one of the many energy wasters? Is valuable heat

leaking out of your _____? Do you drive
                           NOUN

a _____ car, the kind known as a big
        ADJECTIVE

_____ guzzler? Do you want the price of gas to
     A LIQUID

go to _____? Well, you had better
         AN AMOUNT OF MONEY

insulate your _____ right away. Learn to drive
                    NOUN

_____ and never _____
         ADVERB   VERB (PRESENT TENSE)

unless you have to.

Pollution is everyone's problem. The nationally reknowned

scientist, _____, recently said, "The
              NAME OF PERSON IN ROOM

air in American cities is composed of six parts oxygen, one part

_____, and three parts _____.
     A NONSENSE WORD   SOMETHING ICKY

If it gets worse, we won't be able to _____."
                                         VERB (PRESENT TENSE)

If you have a _____ car, be sure to install a
                    ADJECTIVE

_____ on it. And report anyone you see who is
         NOUN

_____.
     VERB ENDING IN "ING"

THE GRADUATION PARTY

We are having a graduation party for _____
NAME OF GIRL IN ROOM

who finally got out of _____. She is only
NAME OF A SCHOOL

_____ years old but looks much older as she is
A NUMBER

wearing a _____ dress and has her hair styled just
ADJECTIVE

like _____. She is here with her boyfriend,
A TV ACTRESS

_____, who just gave her his class
NAME OF BOY IN ROOM

_____. She got some wonderful graduation
NOUN

presents, including a new electric _____-dryer, and
PART OF THE HEAD

a necklace made of genuine _____. After
PLURAL NOUN

we open the presents we are all going to spend the evening

_____.
VERB ENDING IN "ING"

CHESS

Chess is a very ancient game invented by _____
NAME OF PERSON IN ROOM

in the sixth century. It requires _____
ADJECTIVE

concentration and a _____ mind. Chess
ADJECTIVE

is played on a square _____ by moving 32 little
NOUN

_____. The object of the game is to capture
PLURAL NOUN

your opponent's _____. When you threaten it,
NOUN

you must say, "_____." When you win
AN EXCLAMATION

you say, "_____." Chess players must
AN EXCLAMATION

_____ in one place for hours at a time,
VERB (PRESENT TENSE)

which can be very hard on your _____. At this time,
NOUN

the world's champion chess player is _____.
A TV ACTOR

THE RODEO

Rodeos are contests which had their beginnings in the western

part of _____. Cowboys would get together for the annual
 _{A COUNTRY}

roundup of _____ and would brag and drink
 _{AN ANIMAL (PLURAL)}

jugs filled with _____ and sing some of their
 _{A LIQUID}

favorite songs like "Home on the _____."
 _{A KITCHEN APPLIANCE}

In 1888, they started having contests. Cowboys would compete

to determine who was the best bronco _____.
 _{NOUN}

In one of the contests, they would ride with Brahma

_____ and _____
 _{AN ANIMAL (PLURAL)}   _{VERB (PRESENT TENSE)}

_____ cows. The cowboys would bet on how fast
 _{ADJECTIVE}

they could rope a _____. Today, rodeos are
 _{AN ANIMAL}

held in Madison _____ Garden, and winners get
 _{ADJECTIVE}

thousands of dollars and new _____.
 _{PLURAL NOUN}

ALL ABOUT THE LINK TRAINER

A Link Trainer is a _____ airplane that never
                        ADJECTIVE

leaves the _____. It's used to teach beginning
                NOUN

_____ the principles of flying. It has a
     PLURAL NOUN

_____ and a full set of _____
        NOUN   PLURAL NOUN

just like a regular airplane. And it can imitate any sort of aerial

maneuver such as a loop the _____ or a
                                     NOUN

_____ dive. And it is very safe. Nothing can
     ADJECTIVE

happen to you unless, of course, you forget to fasten your safety

_____. Then you might fall out on your
        NOUN

_____. After a student passes the tests on the
        NOUN

Link Trainer, he then gets into a real plane and learns to taxi

down the _____. And he learns to tell which way
              NOUN

the _____ is blowing before he takes off into the
         NOUN

"Wild _____ Yonder!" Then in no time he learns
            A COLOR

to take off and is flying _____ miles per hour at
                               A NUMBER

a height of _____ feet. When he does this he is a
                 A NUMBER

real pilot.

HEALTH QUIZ

Answer the following questions with either a _____
A NONSENSE WORD

or a _____.
ANOTHER NONSENSE WORD

1. Do you brush your _____ at least once every
PLURAL NOUN

_____?
A UNIT OF TIME

2. Do you sleep on a hard _____?
NOUN

3. Do you go see your family _____ and
AN OCCUPATION OR JOB

get a _____ checkup every year?
ADJECTIVE

4. Do you eat a _____ breakfast?
ADJECTIVE

5. Do you take regular exercise such as _____,
VERB ENDING IN "ING"

_____, or _____?
VERB ENDING IN "ING"   VERB ENDING IN "ING"

6. Have you stopped _____ and
VERB ENDING IN "ING"

_____?
VERB ENDING IN "ING"

7. Do you take plenty of vitamins, minerals, and

_____?
PLURAL NOUN

If you answered _____ to more than five of
FIRST NONSENSE WORD USED

the above, you are worse than unhealthy. You are probably dead.

CRAZY DAYS OF SUMMER

In the summertime, it is important to eat _____.
                                              ADVERB

A good _____-weather diet should contain very
              ADJECTIVE

little fat and lots of _____. Ice cream is very
                           PLURAL NOUN

_____ for you. My favorite flavor of ice cream
      ADJECTIVE

is _____. I also like _____-Cola.
        A FOOD   A FRUIT OR VEGETABLE

It is made with carbonated _____ and chocolate
                                  A LIQUID

flavoring and has just a touch of _____.
                                      A CHEMICAL

These things go well with _____ pizza and
                                ADJECTIVE

_____. Other hot weather drinks are iced tea,
      A FOOD

_____-ade, and chocolate malted _____.
  A VEGETABLE   A LIQUID

But remember, after eating, spend at least an hour just

_____ around.
  VERB ENDING IN "ING"

THE FINAL EXAM

Here are some sample questions with _____
_{ADJECTIVE}

answers that may give you an idea what final exams are like:

QUESTION: Who was the first president of the United States?

ANSWER: _____, who was also called, "The
A FAMOUS PERSON

_____ of Our Country."
NOUN

QUESTION: What is the shortest distance between two

_____?
PLURAL NOUN

ANSWER: A straight _____.
NOUN

QUESTION: Who said, "I regret that I only have one

_____ to give for my country."?
NOUN

ANSWER: _____.
A FAMOUS PERSON

QUESTION: If two apples cost _____ cents, how
A NUMBER

much would one _____ cost?
NOUN

ANSWER: What are you? Some kind of a nut or something?

If you answer questions like these, you should end

up with the worst _____ in class.
PLURAL NOUN